We Walk Dogs

By Janice Behrens

No part of this publication can be reproduced in whole or in part, or stored in a retrieval system, or transmitted in any form or by any means, electronic, mechanical, photocopying, recording, or otherwise, without written permission of the publisher. For permission, write to Scholastic Inc., 557 Broadway, New York, NY 10012.

ISBN: 978-1-338-88857-7

Editor: Liza Charlesworth
Art Director: Tannaz Fassihi; Designer: Tanya Chernyak
Photos ©: 5: Roman Samborskyi/Shutterstock.com. All other photos © Getty Images.

Copyright © Scholastic Inc. All rights reserved. Published by Scholastic Inc.

1 2 3 4 5 6 7 8 9 10   68   31 30 29 28 27 26 25 24 23

Printed in Jiaxing, China. First printing, January 2023.

SCHOLASTIC INC.

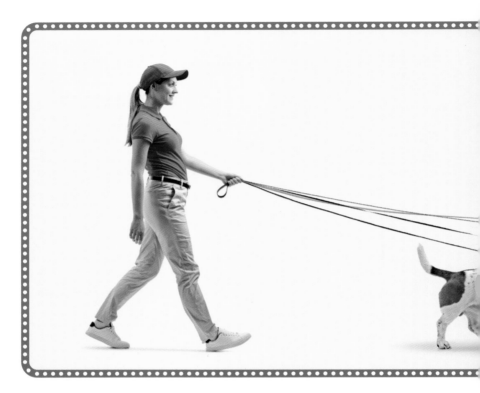

We walk dogs.

Woof, woof.

We walk big dogs.
Woof, woof.

We walk small dogs.
Woof, woof.

We walk fluffy dogs.
Woof, woof.

We walk puppy dogs.
Woof, woof.

But we do not walk cats.
Meow, meow.